Boffin Boy and the Poison Garden
by David Orme

Illustrated by Peter Richardson

Published by Ransom Publishing Ltd.
Radley House, 8 St Cross Road, Winchester, Hants. SO23 9HX
www.ransom.co.uk

ISBN   978 178127 047 9
First published in 2013
Copyright © 2013 Ransom Publishing Ltd.

Illustrations copyright © 2013 Peter Richardson

A CIP catalogue record of this book is available from the British Library.

ABOUT THE AUTHOR

David Orme has written well over 200 books including poetry collections, fiction and non-fiction, and school text books. He especially likes writing science fiction stories, and historical stories set in London. Find out more at: www.magic-nation.com.

She wanted to turn everyone into a tree. She liked trees more than people.

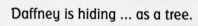

Daffney is hiding ... as a tree.

That thing will never find me now!

Katt returns to normal.
Well done, Katt!
AIEEEEEE!
But how are we going to get out of this cage?

Aargh! What's that? One of my experiments must have gone wrong!
Silly Daffney. It's Katt of course!

One shot of this, and you'll be just like your favourite supermarket!
What do you mean?
You'll have branches everywhere!

You can't make us drink that!
Who said anything about drinking it?

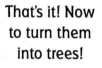

That's it! Now to turn them into trees!

I told you it was a really bad idea!

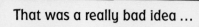

That was a really bad idea …

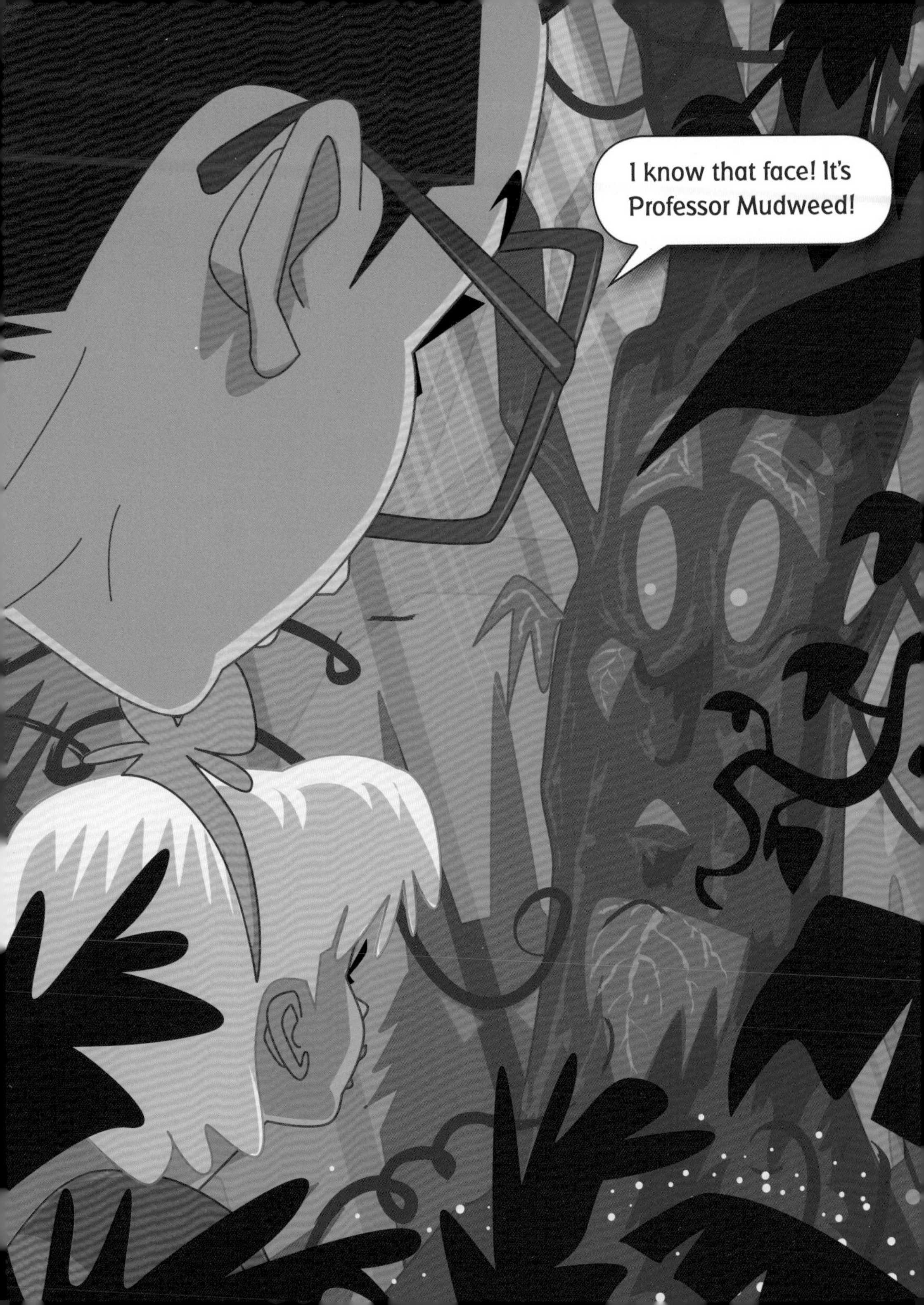
I know that face! It's Professor Mudweed!

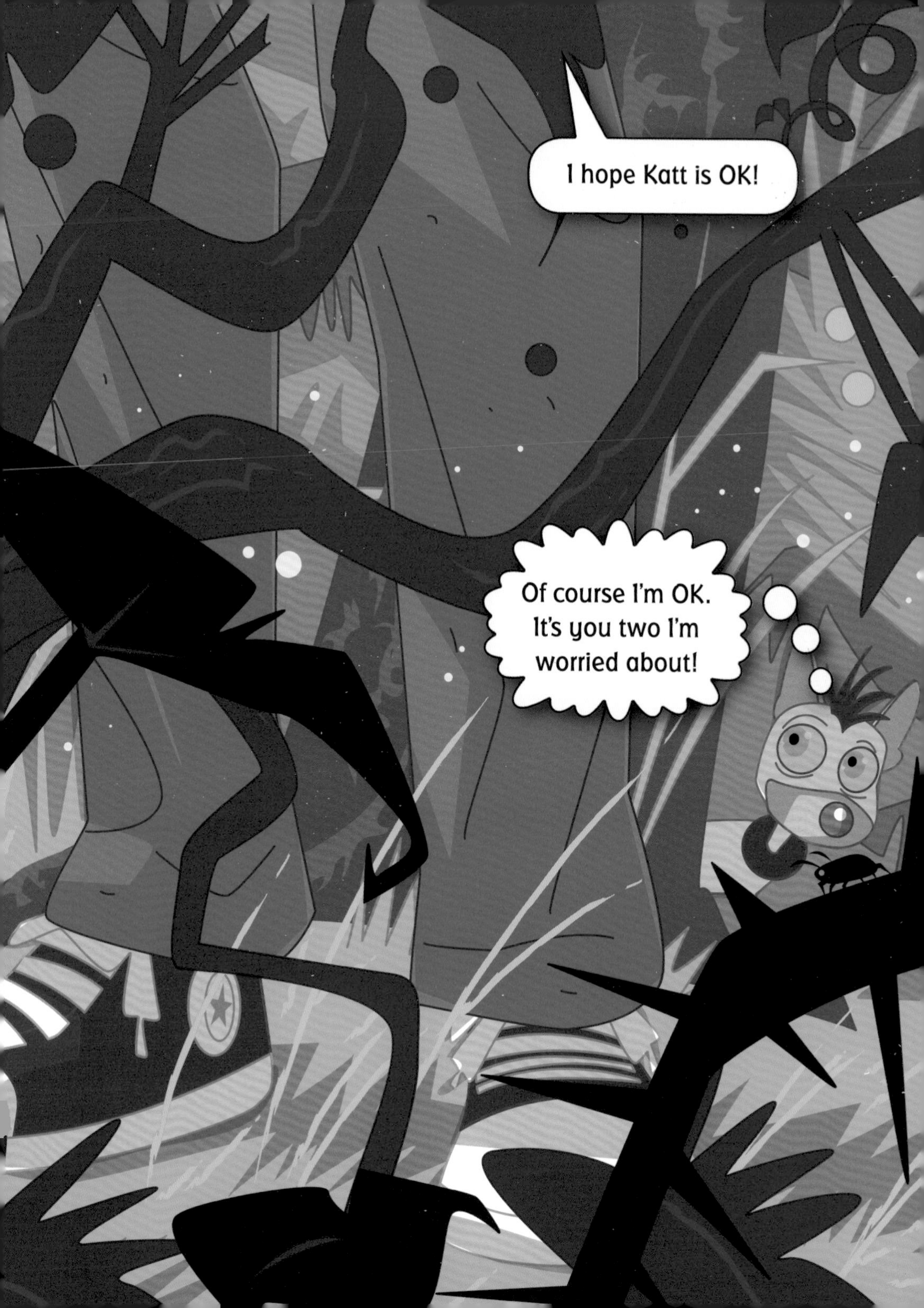
I hope Katt is OK!
Of course I'm OK. It's you two I'm worried about!

These trees look just like dogs!
Wu Pee said she did experiments on dogs!

Boffin Boy and Polly explore the garden ...

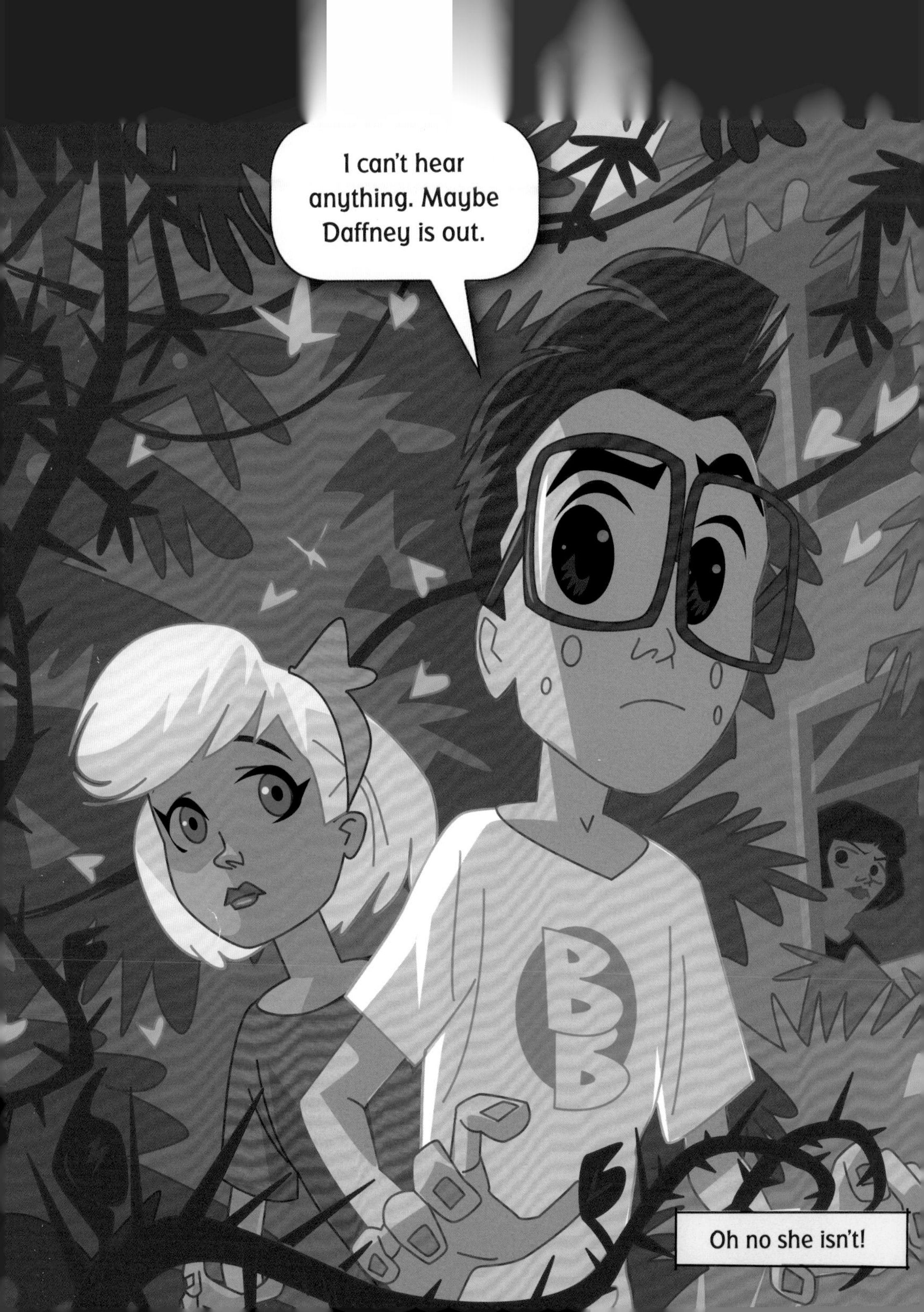
I can't hear anything. Maybe Daffney is out.
Oh no she isn't!

Boffin Boy had brought his door-opening twiddly thing with him …

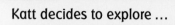
Katt decides to explore …

Katt! Come back!

Boffin Boy decides to check out Doctor Daffney …
Take care, Boffin Boy. Daffney experiments on animals. Even dogs!

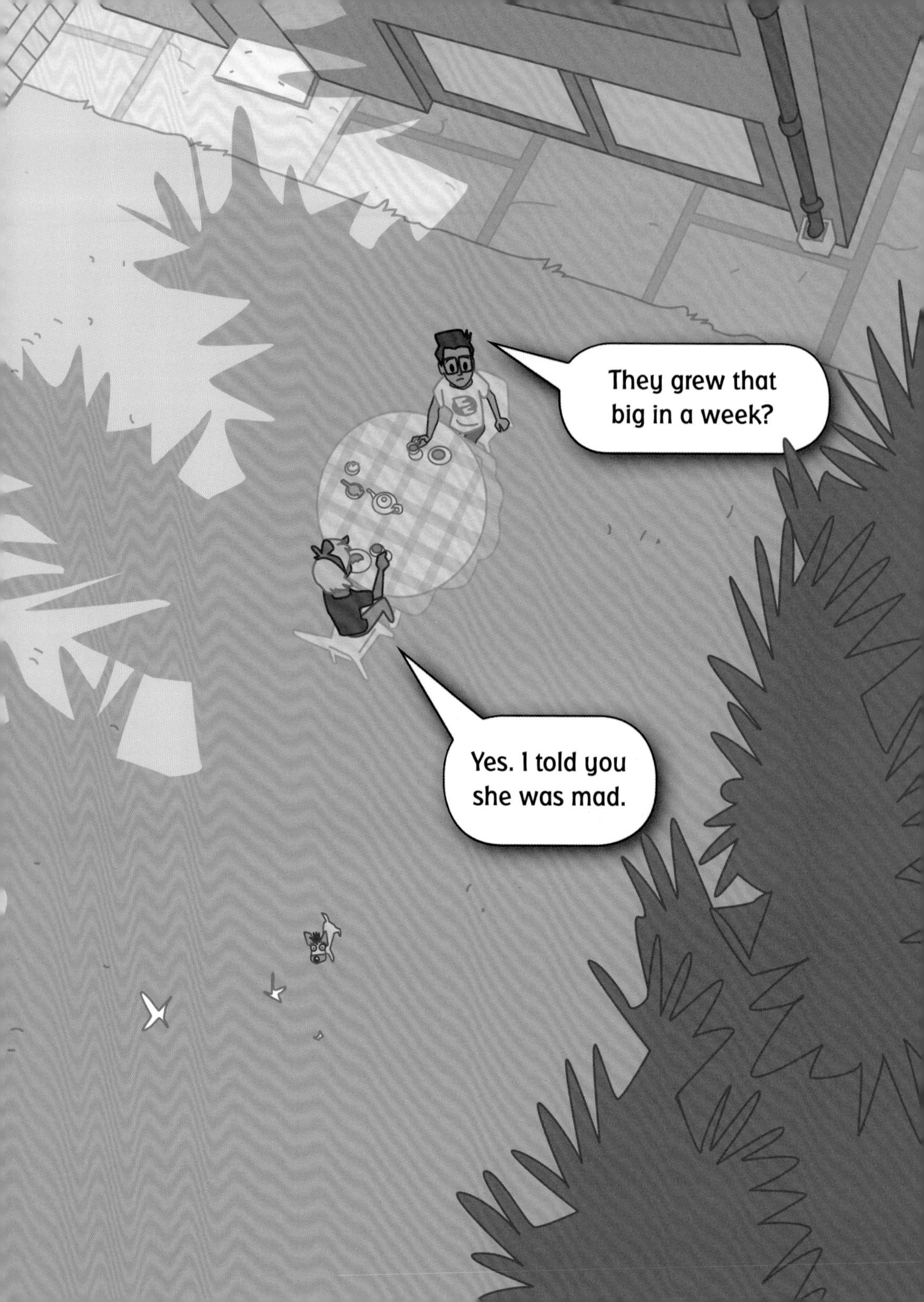
They grew that big in a week?
Yes. I told you she was mad.

Boffin Boy

AND THE

Poison Garden

By David Orme

Illustrated by Peter Richardson

Ransom